Grade 7

The Syllabus of Examinations should be read for details of requirements, especially those for scales, aural tests and sight-reading. Attention should be paid to the Special Notices on the front inside cover, where warning is given of changes.

The syllabus is obtainable from music dealers or from The Associated Board of the Royal Schools of Music, 14 Bedford Square, London WC1B 3JG (please send a stamped addressed C5 envelope).

In overseas centres, information may be obtained from the Local Representative or Resident Secretary.

Requirements

SCALES AND ARPEGGIOS (from memory)

Scales   legato or staccato, as directed by the examiner:
(i)   in similar motion, hands together one octave apart, and each hand separately, in the keys specified in one of the following groups chosen by the candidate (minors in melodic *and* harmonic forms) (four octaves):
Group 1: C, D, E, F♯, B♭, A♭ majors and minors
Group 2: G, A, B, F, E♭, D♭ majors and minors
(ii)   in similar motion, hands together a third apart, in the major and harmonic minor keys of the group chosen for (i) (four octaves)
(iii)   in contrary motion, both hands beginning and ending on the key-note (unison), in the major and harmonic minor keys chosen for (i) (two octaves)
(iv)   legato *only*, in thirds, each hand separately, in the key of C major (two octaves)
(v)   staccato *only*, in sixths, each hand separately (fingered 1 & 5), in the key of C major (two octaves)

Chromatic Scales   legato or staccato, as directed:
(i)   in similar motion, hands together one octave apart, and each hand separately, beginning on any note named by the examiner (four octaves)
(ii)   in contrary motion, hands beginning and ending on the same note (unison), beginning on C and F♯ (two octaves)

Arpeggios   legato *only*, in similar motion, hands together one octave apart, and each hand separately:
(i)   the major and minor common chords, in first inversion *only*, of the keys of the scale group chosen above (four octaves)
(ii)   dominant seventh chords, in root position *only*, in the keys of the scale group chosen above (three octaves)

PLAYING AT SIGHT (see current syllabus)

AURAL TESTS (see current syllabus)

THREE PIECES

Candidates should choose one piece from Group A, one piece from Group B, and the third piece *either* from Group C *or* from the further alternatives listed below:

Editor for the Associated Board: **Richard Jones**

Music origination by Barnes Music Engraving Ltd.
Printed in Great Britain by Headley Brothers Ltd,
The Invicta Press, Ashford, Kent and London.

Where appropriate, pieces have been checked with original source material and edited as necessary for instructional purposes. Fingering, phrasing, pedalling, metronome marks and the editorial realization of ornaments (where given) are for guidance but are not comprehensive or obligatory.

Prelude in G

No. 15, BWV 884/1, from *The Well-Tempered Clavier*, Part II

A:1

J. S. BACH

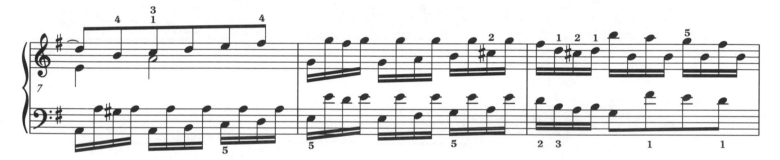

Source: London, British Library, Add. MS 35021.
Dynamics are left to the player's discretion.

Reprinted from J. S. Bach, *The Well-Tempered Clavier*, Part II, edited by Richard Jones (Associated Board)

4

Study in D

Op. 30 No. 33

CRAMER

Vivace [♪ = *c*.72]

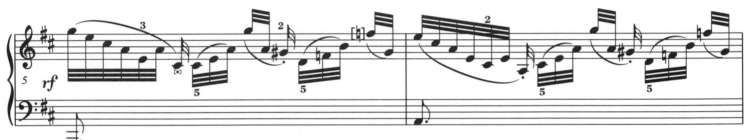

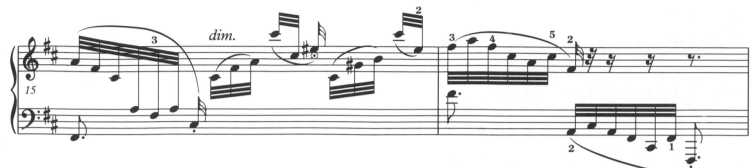

Source: *Studio per il piano forte*, Vol. I, Op. 30 (London, 1804).

Johann Baptist Cramer (1771–1858) was brought to England from Mannheim as a child, settling here and studying the piano with Clementi and C. F. Abel. He established himself as a concert pianist and became renowned for his performances of Bach and Mozart and for his expressive legato touch.

Allegro

Third movement from Sonata in C, K. 279

Edited by
Stanley Sadie and Denis Matthews

MOZART

Source: autograph, formerly in the Preussische Staatsbibliothek, Berlin.
The Sonata in C, K. 279, is Mozart's earliest surviving piano sonata, dating from 1775 when he was nineteen years old. Mozart repeated dynamics for both staves, and this has been retained to clarify the intention in bars 38, 81, 124, 126, 139 and 141.

Andante

Second movement from Sonata in D, Op. 28

BEETHOVEN

Source: *Grande Sonate pour le Pianoforte*, Op. 28 (Vienna, 1802).
This sonata, which is said to have been a favourite of Beethoven's, was written in 1801 and nicknamed the 'Pastorale' by the publisher Cranz.
Small inconsistencies of phrasing and articulation have been ironed out by the editor.

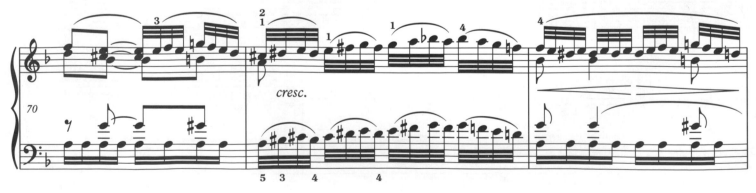

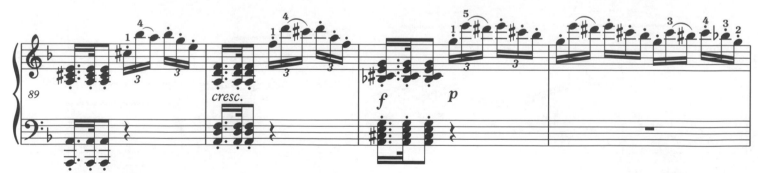

C:1

Twilight
Op. 12

SULLIVAN

Andante quasi allegretto [♩. = *c.*44]

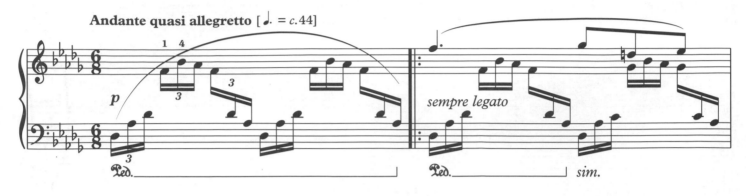

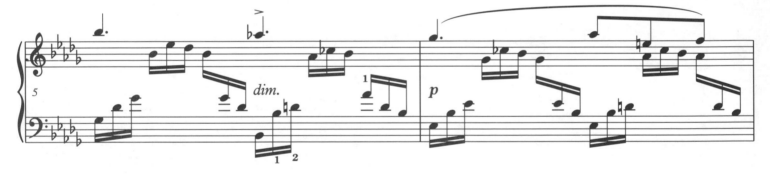

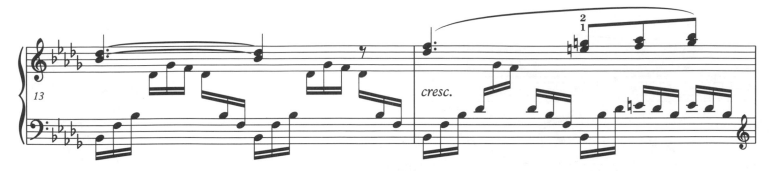

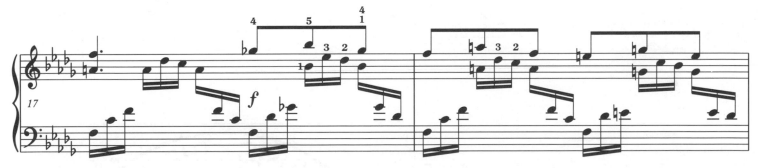

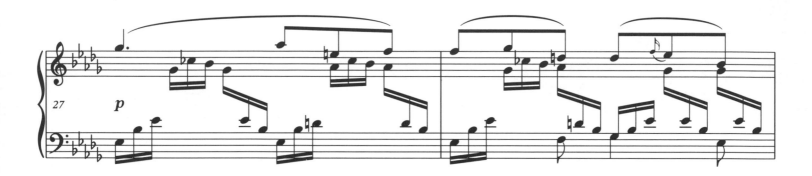

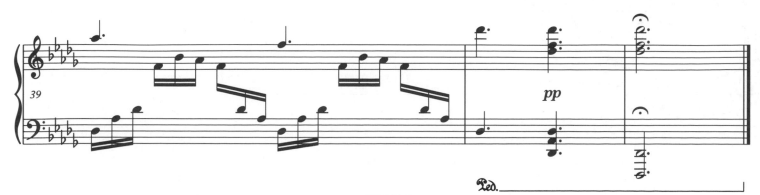

C:2

Coda

No. 6 from *Villageoises*

POULENC

en   cédant   un peu

* *8ve double* = two octaves higher